Taylor

# HAPPY AT THE Bel-Air

DOVE
BOOKS

# HAPPY AT THE Bel-Air

**HOTEL Bel-Air**

701 STONE CANYON ROAD ● LOS ANGELES, CALIFORNIA 90077

| LAST NAME | FIRST NAME | ROOM TYPE | DAILY RATE | ARRIVAL DATE | DEPARTURE DATE | ROOM NUMBER |
|---|---|---|---|---|---|---|
| | | | | | | |

## REGISTRATION INFORMATION

| LAST NAME | FIRST NAME | ROOM | DAILY RATE | ARRIVAL DATE | DEPARTURE DATE | ROOM NUMBER |
|---|---|---|---|---|---|---|
| HAPPY | | | | | | |

| | | | GUESTS | ARRIVAL TIME | NO. ROOMS | ACCOUNT NUMBER |
|---|---|---|---|---|---|---|

STREET

COMMENTS

| CITY | ST. | ZIP CODE |
|---|---|---|

PAYMENT

| CASH | VISA | M.C | A.X | D.C | C.B | COMPANY |
|---|---|---|---|---|---|---|
| ☐ | ☐ | ☐ | ☐ | ☐ | ☐ | ☐ |

| COMPANY NAME | ATTN | ADDRESS | CITY | ZIP CODE |
|---|---|---|---|---|

A SAFE IS PROVIDED FOR DEPOSIT OF VALUABLES. THE HOTEL CANNOT BE RESPONSIBLE FOR VALUABLES NOT DEPOSITED. THE GUEST HEREBY ACCEPTS FULL LIABILITY FOR CHARGES.

SIGNATURE

## BY GWEN DAVIS    PHOTOS BY SONIA MOSKOWITZ

ISBN 0-7871-0599-6

Printed in Mexico

Dove Books
301 North Cañon Drive
Beverly Hills, CA 90210

Distributed by Penguin USA

Text design and layout by Rick Penn-Kraus
Cover design by Rick Penn-Kraus
Cover photograph by Sonia Moskowitz

First Printing: January 1996

10 9 8 7 6 5 4 3 2 1

To Frank Bowling

*I* have worked a long time in Hollywood, and I've seen a lot of dogs. Lassie, Lady, The Tramp, Beethoven, Benji, Won Ton Ton, The Dog Who Saved Hollywood. All of them stars.

But never have I known a dog like Happy. For all of his talent, modest, even humble. A dog who can look contrite. The only one, in my experience, who is both questing for spiritual truth, and has dined at Spago.

In this, his first recorded adventure, Happy goes to the Bel-Air Hotel to heal a broken heart. But his stay becomes a journey of self-discovery, a trip to Enlightenment. The discoveries he makes are a joyful, uplifting lesson for us all, children and so-called adults alike.

The world could use a few more people like Happy.

Like many in the world, Happy was sad.
Life hadn't turned out quite the way he'd expected.

So he decided to leave
his cares behind him

**and spend a few days at the Hotel Bel-Air**

putting on the dog.

He didn't have a lot of money,

but he'd cross that bridge when he came to it.

Once in his lovely room, he felt even lonelier.

Meals were slightly sorrowful, eating alone . . .

Juliet! Juliet!
Wherefore art thou,
Juliet?

True, there were those who seemed to care,
but they weren't his kind of girl.

Then, one day by Swan Lake, he spied . . .

Petunia!

But she had her nose in the air.

So he sent himself to her in a basket of flowers.

But they caught him!

And the manager told him
never to darken that basket again.

Then he hid himself in a room service tray,

hoping to be
delivered,

but it was to the wrong room.

Why was she so aloof, his lovely Petunia?
He had to find out!

Then he spied her with her rich protector,

who covered her with jewels.

What could Happy
do but speak
from the heart?
"Money isn't
everything,"
he wrote.
"I love you!
Will you marry me!?"

He had himself groomed to be Groom

and waited for
his Bride…
and waited…
and waited.

But she
never came.

He tried jogging to work off his depression.

What could he do
to win her?
He was really
out on a limb.

Maybe if he acted like a tough guy . . .

or a good old boy…

or a big Hollywood producer, she would come to love him.

And dreaming of the ways he could capture
her heart, he fell fast asleep.

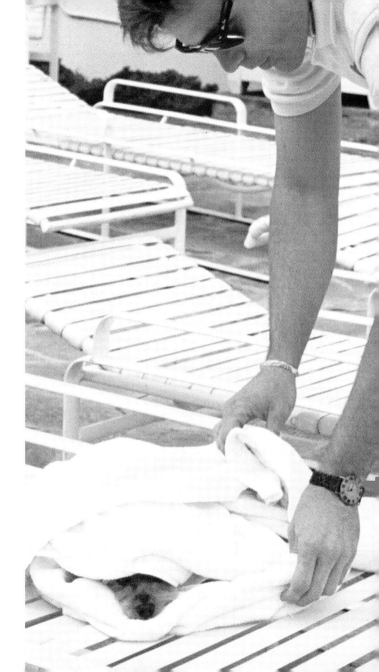

The pool boy came
to clean up
and didn't see him,

and put him in a basket with the towels.

So Happy ended up in the laundry.
It was a true cleansing…

An Awakening!

For he understood
that freedom is being
exactly who you are.

And just to be in a beautiful place

is a state of grace.

And we all have the choice between being unHappy

and Happy.

*J*ust like Toto, Happy was born in Kansas. But he immediately moved to Beverly Hills, where he lived with a seemingly normal family, before beginning his travels. He studied at Bryn Mawr College, where he wrote a book of poems. He has resided in St. Tropez, San Francisco, Weinheim, Rome, New York, Amsterdam, La Jolla  and Vienna, returning in a coat pocket on an airline that didn't permit pets. This is the same coat pocket he hid in the night he dined at Hollywood's famed Spago. He currently resides in Bel-Air. He knows he's not in Kansas anymore.